SAMMY
IN THE SWIM

written by Neil Mor
illustrated by Geoffrey E

MACDONALD

Far out at sea there lives a colony of seals on Icecold Island.

Sammy the seal pup lives there, on his own rock near his mother.

Every day Sammy's mother goes for a swim,
But Sammy never wants to go in with her.

How many seals are swimming?
How many mother seals are there? How many pups?
And how many seals are there altogether?

Sammy doesn't like the water. It's cold and wet, and tastes salty.

He is sad without his mother, so his three
penguin friends try to cheer him up.

Sammy tells the penguins that he wishes
he could swim like them.

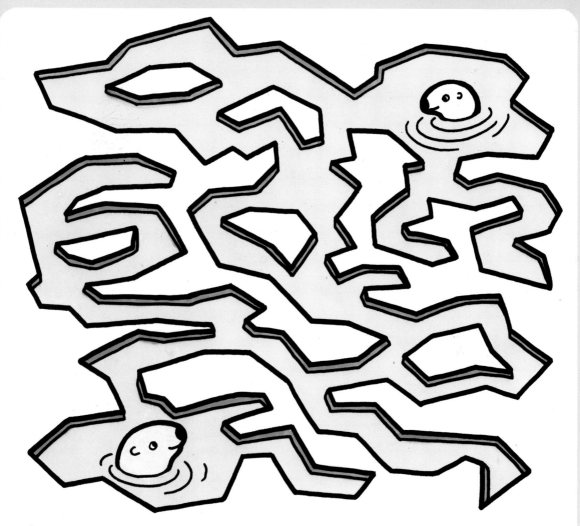

Which way must the mother seal swim to reach her pup?
And which way must the pup swim to reach his mother?
Find the path with your finger.

Big penguins like big fish, and little penguins like little fish.
Share out all the fish, with one for each penguin.

A gull lands on Sammy's rock to warn
him that a storm is on the way.

The storm makes the sea very choppy, and Sammy watches the waves getting higher and higher.

How many gulls are there?
How many are floating on the water?
How many are flying? And how many are on the rock?

Suddenly a giant wave sweeps Sammy off his rock.

The storm carries him out to sea and
Sammy is very frightened.

Just then a big flipper catches him and
helps him to swim.

Find the different coloured pairs of fishes.
Which fish is left as the odd one out?

Sammy recognises the big seal who saved him—it's his father!

But with a sudden splash he's gone again.

Sammy dives down to follow his father. He feels at home in the water now.

Find the shadow to go with each animal.

Sammy and his father meet Grosso the whale, who lives right out at sea.

Which two whales are the same size?
And which two fish are the same size?

At the bottom of the sea there are lots of new and exciting things to look at.

Which starfish is the odd one out?

Which sea anemone?

Which seaweed? And which crab?

On their way home they stop to see Sammy's penguin friends playing on an iceberg.

When they reach their rock, Sammy's
mother wants to hear all about his adventure.

**But now that he can swim, Sammy doesn't
ever want to come out of the water!**